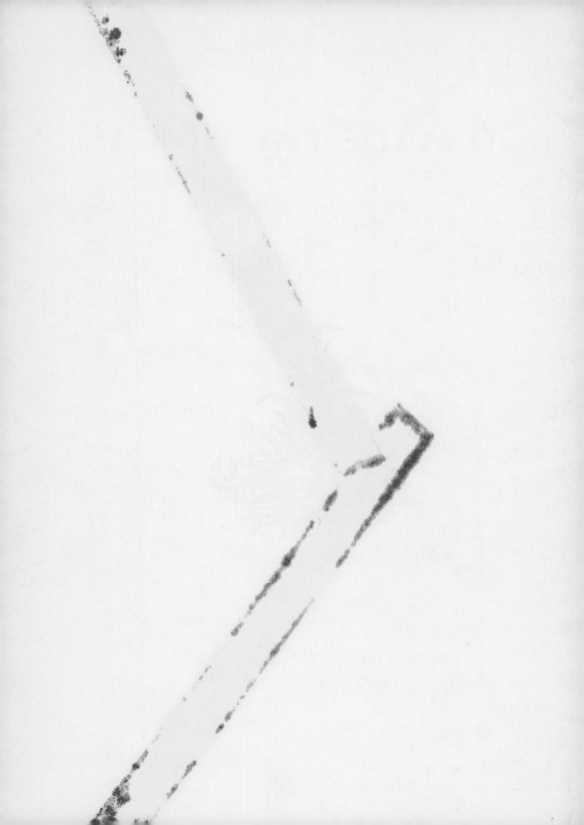

GOD MADE THE WORLD

By Pelagie Doane

J. B. LIPPINCOTT COMPANY

Philadelphia   *New York*

For
Sis and Ron

God made the whole world

and He is in everything He ever made.

He made the great blue sky
and the fleecy clouds.

He made the earth
and the sun to warm it.

He made the daytime for playing
and the nighttime for dreaming.

He put the moon and stars in the night sky
so we can see them if we waken.

He made hills for grass and for sheep
and for romping.

He made mountains for climbing
and stones for building.
He made rocks where snakes may sun themselves.

He made Winter.

He made Spring.

He made Summer.

He made Fall.

He made trees with long branches
and green leaves;
some have nuts and some have apples.

They have places for birds' nests
and limbs for climbing.

He made grass
to run on
and dream on.

God
made flowers
for bees
and for
picking.

God made all the animals:
big ones, wild ones,
and cuddly ones;

some in shells,
some in hides,
but most in furry coats.

He made birds to sing,
and ears for us to hear them.

He made brooks for fish and frogs
and for wading.

God made the sea for ships to sail on

and waves to roll in.

God
made rain
for the garden
seeds,
for corn and
beans and potatoes,

and He made puddles
to splash in.

He made snow,

one flake at a time
and each one different.

God made grown-up people
to work and to laugh.

He made babies, soft and round,
with curled up fingers.

He made mothers and fathers

and He made me.